The Good, the Bad and the Bungle

David Walke

Stanley Thornes (Publishers) Ltd

Contents

Originally published in 1979 by Hutchinson Education
Reprinted 1980, 1982, 1984, 1985, 1988, 1989

Reprinted 1990 by
Stanley Thornes (Publishers) Ltd
Ellenborough House
Wellington Street
CHELTENHAM GL50 1YD
England

Reprinted 1993, 1994

British Library Cataloguing in Publication Data

Walke, David
    The good, the bad and the bungle
    – (Spirals series; 2)
    1. Readers – Drama
    I. Title   II. Series
    428'.6'2   PE1121

    ISBN 0 7487 0372 1

Cover illustration by Simon Rees
Cover design by Ned Hoste

Set in IBM Pyramid
Illustrations by Martin Williams
Printed and bound in Great Britain at Martin's The Printers, Berwick.

The Job

The Job

Three characters: *Boss, Flash* and *Billy*

Flash   Hello, Boss.

Boss   Hello, boys.

Billy   Hello, Boss. It's good to see you, Boss.

Boss   It's good to be out, Billy

Flash   It's been a long time.

Boss   It has, and doing time is no fun, Flash.

Flash   You're right.

Billy   No fun at all.

Boss   It was hard luck the cops got me.

Flash   Real hard, Boss.

Boss   It's the last time I pinch a car.

Billy   Pity it was a cop car, Boss.

Flash   Yes, Boss, funny you didn't see the blue light on the top when you tried to pinch it.

Billy   Or the two coppers sitting in the back.

Boss   Well, you know what it's like, boys. I was in a hurry, it was dark, I needed a car. I found one that wasn't locked, so I was into

4

it. Then, BANG.

Flash	That was a bit of bad luck, Boss.
Billy	You've always had bad luck, Boss.
Boss	Always.
Flash	Think of the time you opened that new supermarket.
Billy	Did you open a new supermarket, Boss?
Boss	Yes, Billy.
Billy	TV stars open new supermarkets too.
Flash	Not with a crow-bar, Billy.
Boss	I've had no luck at all. All I want is a break.
Flash	(All he wants is a brain!)
Boss	What was that, Flash?
Flash	Er, nothing, Boss. I just said, 'Yes, all you want is a break.'
Billy	I think all you need is a break-in, boss. Get it? A break-in.
Boss	What are you on about, Billy?
Flash	I think it was a joke, Boss.
Boss	I don't need jokes. I need money.
Billy	Flash has got money, Boss. He's doing well these days. He's got a car, a big Jag.

Boss	You're doing well are you, Flash?
Flash	Not bad.
Boss	What racket are you into then?
Flash	I buy and sell. A nod here, a wink there, and a tenner in the pocket.
Boss	I see, you're going up in the world.
Flash	I'm doing OK.
Boss	Well don't forget, I'm the boss of this outfit.
Flash	I won't forget, Boss. You're the boss, Boss.
Boss	I'm the brains.
Flash	Oh yes, Boss, you've got the brains (and some day you'll find them)!
Boss	What was that?
Flash	I said, 'That's just fine then.'
Boss	It's not fine at all. I need some cash.
Flash	I can lend you some.
Boss	Come on, Flash, I'm an honest crook. I don't borrow, I pinch my own cash.
Billy	Why don't you ask for a sub on your old-age pension, Boss?
Boss	Don't be silly, Billy. I'm only 48.
Flash	You don't look a day over 63, Boss.

Boss	48 years old and not a penny to my name.
Billy	Never mind, Boss.
Boss	I've never had any money. We were so poor when I was a kid that my mother used to sell clothes-pegs to the gypsies.
Billy	We'll help you, Boss.
Boss	We never even had a fire at home. If we were cold my dad used to suck a mint. We all sat round his tongue to get warm.
Flash	This is breaking my heart.
Boss	The rent man had to come to our house in a tank to get his money.
Flash	I can hear violins, I'm sure I can.
Boss	I can remember going to the butcher's with my mother.
Flash	I think he's cracking up, Billy.
Boss	And my mother says to the butcher, 'Give us a sheep's head and leave the legs on.'
Billy	The poor old lady.
Boss	And the butcher says, 'I'll leave the eyes in, they'll see you through the week.'
Billy	If you need money, Boss, why don't you get a job?

Boss	Oh no, Billy, not a job. That's no good. You see, I have trouble with my back.
Flash	He can't get it off the bed.
Boss	Watch it, clever Dick!
Flash	OK, Boss, OK.
Billy	Have you never had a job, Boss?
Boss	Never, Billy. When I was a kid I wanted to be a tree doctor, but I faint at the sight of sap. So that was no good.
Billy	So what did you do then?
Boss	Well, my old man said to me, 'If at first you don't succeed, cheat!' So I started on a life of crime.
Flash	Yes, Boss, you put your foot on the bottom step of the ladder. Then you worked your way down.
Boss	Are you taking the mick?
Flash	Me, Boss? No, Boss. I'm just trying to tell you how to do it. Get a good racket going. Go for the right job at the right time.
Boss	Look, Flash, I'm the boss. I know what to do. Don't try to teach your grandmother to suck eggs.
Billy	Has she got no teeth then, Boss?

Boss	What the heck are you on about?
Billy	Well, why does she have to suck eggs?
Flash	Shut up, Billy.
Billy	My grandmother uses her teeth to crack nuts.
Boss	You're round the bend.
Billy	I'm not. It's true. She takes them out, bungs in a nut, gives them a thump and there it is, cracked!
Flash	You're the one who's cracked, Billy.
Billy	I'm not!
Boss	Stop it, you two. Just cut it out. I didn't get you here today to mess about.
Flash	What did you get us here for then, Boss?
Boss	I've got a job!
Billy	But you said you didn't like working, Boss.
Boss	Not that kind of a job, Billy, I mean a real job!
Flash	You know his kind of job, Billy. He means pinching stuff.
Boss	Yes, and this, boys, this is the big one.
Billy	The big one?
Boss	Yes, this is it. No more messing about. We're going right to the top.

Billy	What is it, Boss?
Flash	Yes, Boss, don't hang about, tell us.
Boss	It's Blackpool Tower.
Flash	What, Blackpool Tower, Boss?
Boss	Yes, Blackpool Tower.
Flash	We're going to pinch Blackpool Tower?
Billy	It's a bit big, Boss.
Flash	Won't they see us?
Billy	We'll never get it in the van.
Flash	And we'll need a hell of a spanner.
Boss	Hold it, dummies, hold it.
Billy	What's up, Boss?
Boss	I don't mean pinch it, dummies. I mean sell it.
Flash	How do you mean, Boss?
Billy	How can we sell it? It's not ours.
Boss	You know that, Flash knows that, and I know that, but the sucker we sell it to doesn't.
Billy	But what do we want to sell it for anyway?

Boss	For scrap!
Flash	You mean we sell it to a scrap-man?
Boss	Yes. We sell it for scrap to a scrap-man!
Billy	Well, how's he going to get it into his van?
Boss	That's his problem.
Flash	Won't he think it's a bit funny, us selling him Blackpool Tower?
Boss	Not if we do it right.
Flash	How do we do it right, Boss?
Billy	I still think it's a bit big.
Boss	Will you two shut up! I'd be better off nicking the Crown Jewels on my own than doing a job with you two.
Billy	Are we going to sell the Crown Jewels for scrap too, Boss?
Flash	I think the Americans like that sort of stuff.
Boss	Just shut up and listen.
Billy	OK, Boss.
Flash	Real cool, Boss.
Boss	Now then, Fred Scott is a scrap-man. He's a big scrap-man. He's got plenty of money. Big house, big car, big head.

Flash	Is that him with the big house out by the golf course?
Boss	The very same.
Flash	They say he lights his fags with five-pound notes.
Billy	Can't he afford a lighter?
Flash	You thick twit, Billy.
Boss	Now this is my plan. I ring him up. I tell him I'm from the town hall. I tell him they're going to sell Blackpool Tower for scrap because it's getting old and they want to build a new one. What do you think?
Flash	I don't know, Boss. Will it work?
Boss	Yes, it will work. Fred Scott will do any-thing to make more money. He'll jump at the chance to get Blackpool Tower.
Billy	It made me jump, Boss.
Boss	What did?
Billy	When you said we were going to pinch Blackpool Tower. It made me jump.
Flash	What if it turns bad on us, Boss? We might end up getting nicked.
Boss	No we won't, it's the best plan I ever had.

Billy	I think the one about the Crown Jewels was better.
Flash	It's too risky, Boss.
Billy	We won't even need a van for the Crown Jewels.
Flash	Fred Scott might know who you are.
Billy	We could get the jewels in a box and just carry them out.
Boss	Listen, I'm the boss. I make the plans, so cut out the chat.
Billy	OK, Boss.
Boss	Now we need one other person for this job.
Billy	Who's that, Boss?
Boss	There's only one man who can do it. One man who can make the plan work.
Flash	Who is it, Boss?
Boss	Crusher!
Flash	Not Crusher! How does he fit in?
Boss	Well, we give Fred Scott the story about scrapping Blackpool Tower. We chat him up. We offer it to him at a good price. But if he doesn't like the idea, if we can't sway him, Crusher steps in.

Flash	And what does Crusher do?
Boss	Hits him.
Billy	We've got a bit of a problem there, Boss.
Boss	How's that?
Billy	Crusher's been done, he's been locked up.
Boss	When?
Billy	Last month.
Boss	What for?
Billy	Well, he was just picking up a brick from that building site next to the gas-works. Then he was going down to the jeweller's in the High Street. He was going to put the brick through the window and grab what he could.
Flash	So the cops got Crusher for 'smash and grab'?
Billy	No, he never made it to the jeweller's.
Flash	What happened then?
Billy	He got nicked for pinching a brick from the building site.
Boss	Well that's that then. We'll have to forget Blackpool Tower. That's another plan up the creek.

The Van

The Van

Three characters: *Boss*, *Billy* and *Crusher*

Billy	Hello, Boss.
Boss	Hello, Billy.
Billy	So you've got the next job fixed up, Boss?
Boss	I've got it fixed up for tomorrow night, Billy.
Billy	What is it, then? What's the job?
Boss	Old Smith's place, the box factory. The safe will be stuffed full of cash tomorrow night. We just have to crack the safe.
Billy	So that's why you asked for a van?
Boss	Yes, for a fast get-away.
Billy	Well, I've got you a van. This is it.
Boss	This thing?
Billy	Yes, Boss.
Boss	It's a bit old, isn't it?
Billy	It's only had one other owner.
Boss	Who was that, Queen Victoria?
Billy	No, my old man.

Boss	But your old man can't drive.
Billy	I know, but he keeps his ferrets in it.
Boss	Trust your old man to keep ferrets in a van.
Billy	Well, he has to keep them somewhere.
Boss	And where does the horse go?
Billy	He hasn't got a horse as well, Boss.
Boss	What I mean is, where's the horse that pulls the van?
Billy	You don't have a horse for it, Boss. It's got an engine.
Boss	You don't say! And the tyres, did you ever check the tyres?
Billy	Yes, Boss, there are four. You can check them yourself.
Boss	For air, you fool. You check them for air.
Billy	Come on, I'll start her up.
Boss	Just a minute, Billy, I think there's something wrong with this door.
Billy	What's that, Boss?
Boss	It doesn't fall off.
Billy	It's a smart van really, Boss. I'll show you.
Boss	What's this big hole in the floor?

Billy	That's to let in fresh air.
Boss	I bet. Come on then, let's go.
Billy	OK, Boss, as soon as I find the string.
Boss	What's the string for?
Billy	The string is tied to the brick.
Boss	What brick, Billy?
Billy	The brick under the back wheel.
Boss	And what's that for, Billy?
Billy	To stop the car from rolling away.
Boss	Do you mean this car has got no brakes?
Billy	Oh yes, Boss, it's got brakes. Of course it's got brakes. It's just that they don't work.
Boss	Don't work? The brakes don't work?
Billy	Well, sometimes they do, sometimes they don't.
Boss	And what the heck do we do when they don't?
Billy	Well, we try to sort of bump it along the kerb to stop. And if that doesn't work, we throw the brick out.
Boss	Oh no!

Billy	Shall we go for a ride now, Boss?
Boss	Why not, what have I got to lose? An arm perhaps, a leg, or maybe just a couple of teeth.
Billy	See, Boss, it goes along OK.
Boss	Yes, it's not bad, when you get it started.
Billy	Hey look, isn't that Crusher over there, by the bus-stop?
Boss	Yes, that's Crusher. You can't miss Crusher. He looks like the back end of a bus.
Billy	Or a cross between Kojak and King Kong.
Boss	They must have let him out, then.
Billy	I'll stop and see if he wants a lift.
Boss	Crusher's so big that you'll have to give him a tow, not a lift.
Billy	Hello, Crusher, how's things?
Crusher	Terrible.
Boss	Do you want a lift, Crusher?
Crusher	I won't say no.
Billy	Hop in the back then.
Crusher	Thanks.
Boss	This is going to give the springs hell.

Crusher OK, I'm in.

Billy Where are you going, Crusher?

Crusher Just down the High Street. To the bank.

Boss OK, Billy, we'll give Crusher a lift to the bank.

Billy Right, Boss. Here we go. Clutch in. Gear in. Clutch out. Foot down.

Crusher Watch it, Billy. You've just backed into the bus-stop.

Billy Sorry, I'll try again.

Boss Forwards, Billy. Make it go forwards this time.

Billy Clutch in. Gear in. Get in, blast you.

Crusher Watch it, Billy.

Billy Will you get in, you rotten gear! Clutch out! Foot down!

Crusher Shall I get out and thump it?

Boss No, Crusher. Now take it easy, Billy.

Billy That's it. Off we go.

Crusher I had a car that didn't go, so I used to hit it with a hammer.

Boss And did that make it go?

20

Crusher No, but it made me feel a lot better.

Billy How's life then, Crusher?

Crusher Rotten. I had the law round this morning.

Boss What did they want?

Crusher This copper said my dog had been chasing an old lady on a bike.

Billy And had he?

Crusher No, of course not. My dog hasn't got a bike.

Boss Very funny. Is that the big black dog with one ear and no teeth?

Crusher That's him. He's a good watch-dog.

Billy How can he be a good watch-dog, Crusher? He's got no teeth!

Crusher Well, he can give you a very nasty suck.

Boss Nice one.

Billy I'll turn left here and go down the High Street.

Boss I wish you'd stop bumping the kerb, Billy.

Billy It's OK, Boss, you're safe with me.

Crusher Safe? Where did you learn to drive, Billy? At a stock-car rally?

Billy   OK, I'll slow down.

Boss   Yes, and watch those traffic lights, they're going red.

Billy   Right, Boss. Here we go, up to the lights. . and stop.

Boss   Well done. Now they're going to yellow. Get ready.

Billy   Right, Boss.

Boss   Now they're green, off you go.

Billy   Just a minute, Boss.

Crusher   Come on, Billy, they're green, get going.

Billy   Hang on.

Boss   Now they're yellow again.

Billy   Sorry, Boss.

Crusher   Now they're back at red. What's the matter, Billy, haven't they got a colour you like?

Billy   No, I'm having trouble with the gears again.

Crusher   Kick it, Billy, kick the gear stick.

Billy   It's OK, I think I've got it now.

Boss   There's the green light. Let's get out of here.

Billy   Right, Boss.

Crusher If you just drop me here, I'll pop into the bank.

Boss So you need a bit of cash, do you, Crusher?

Crusher Yes, the old woman wants a new coat.

Billy There you are, Crusher, I'll stop here.

Crusher I won't be a minute. If you hang on I'll get some money, then we can go down the pub.

Boss OK, Crusher, but we can't stop here. That's against the law. We'll just go round the block and meet you back here.

Crusher OK.

Billy Right, Boss, do you want me to drive round the block?

Boss Yes, Billy. Now remember, I said round the block, not through it.

Billy This van goes like a bomb, doesn't it, Boss?

Boss Yes, Billy. In fact with the noise it makes, I expect it to blow up any minute.

Billy Look, it's a real smart van.

Boss Smart? It's only the rust that's holding it together.

Billy Now, I'll turn left here and we're back in the High Street.

Boss	There's Crusher just coming out of the bank. Stop here.
Billy	OK, Boss.
Boss	Hop in, Crusher.
Crusher	Thanks, lads.
Billy	Did you get your money, Crusher?
Crusher	Yes, I got it.
Boss	So you can get your old woman a coat now.
Crusher	Yes, she's always wanting something.
Billy	My mum's like that too.
Boss	Isn't it a long way for you to come for some money, Crusher? Isn't there a bank nearer home?
Crusher	Yes, there's a bank just down the bottom of our street.
Billy	Well, why don't you use that one?
Boss	Yes, then you wouldn't have to come all this way for money.
Crusher	Well, they all know me at the bank down our street.
Boss	How do you mean, Crusher?
Crusher	Well, they know my face.

Billy So what, Crusher? What if they do know your face?

Crusher Well, it's daft doing a bank when they know my face.

Boss ...Er...what do you mean when you say, 'doing a bank', Crusher?

Crusher Well, you know, I can't do a bank when they know who I am.

Boss Em, pardon me for asking, Crusher, but when you went into that bank just now, you did cash a cheque? You did use a cheque to get some money, didn't you?

Crusher No, I just grabbed the little chap behind the counter. I told him that if he didn't give me some money, I'd smash his face in.

Boss Oh, no! You must be kidding!

Billy Do you mean you've just robbed the bank, Crusher?

Crusher That's about it.

Boss And here we are helping you to get away. We're even giving you a lift.

Crusher Thanks very much.

Boss No, I don't mean it like that! You've dropped us in it, right up to our necks. Why didn't you tell us!

Crusher I didn't want to spoil your day.

Boss We wanted to keep clear of the cops for a bit.

Billy But now there's one following us!

Boss What?!?

Crusher Yes, there he is, a copper on a motor-bike, and he's after us. Go faster, Billy.

Billy Right. Hang on!

Boss If you hang on to anything in this van it comes off in your hand.

Crusher Come on, Billy, he's getting closer.

Billy He's flashing us, Boss. What shall I do? I can't go any faster.

Boss You'd better stop.

Crusher Yes, Billy, stop. I'll see if I can bluff it out.

Billy OK. Whoops!

Boss What's the matter?

Billy The brakes won't work.

Crusher What, no brakes?

Boss Its OK, Crusher, they'll work in the end. Try them again, Billy.

Billy   I am trying, Boss. They won't work. Hang on, I'll try throwing out the brick on the string.

Crusher What does he mean, 'the brick on the string'?

Boss   Don't throw it, Billy!! Too late, there it goes. But the string's broken.

Billy   Oh no, that trick hasn't worked, we haven't stopped.

Crusher Look out, Billy, I think the copper's going to pass us.

Billy   Yes, here he comes, I can see him.

Boss   He's pulling over in front of us, Billy. He's flagging us down.

Billy   But I can't stop!

Crusher That copper's right in front of us. You'll have to stop!

Billy   But I can't!

Boss   You'll have to do something, Billy. The copper's pulling up right in front of us.

Crusher Watch it, Billy!

Billy   Get out of the way you daft copper! Don't stop there! Can't you tell I've got no brakes!

Boss   He can't hear you, you twit!

Crusher Watch it, Billy! You're going to hit him!

        BANG

Billy We hit him!

Boss Oh no!

Crusher Well, that's one less on the road.

Boss We've had it, hitting a copper.

Crusher Serves him right. It was a daft place to stop.

Billy But we're still going. Where shall I drive to now?

Boss How about South America?

Crusher You made a real mess of his bike.

Billy I hope I didn't hurt him.

Boss The last I saw of him, he was flying through the air.

Billy Hello, what's all that banging?

Boss It sounds like something up with the engine.

Billy Or maybe it's the brakes. It's a heck of a noise.

Crusher I don't think it's coming from the engine.

Boss No, you're right. It sounds more like something on the roof.

Crusher Yes, like something banging on the roof.

Billy I wonder what it is?

Boss Try the brakes again, Billy. See if you can stop and we'll have a look.

Billy Hey, they work!

Crusher It must have been the good thump they got from that motor-bike.

Billy Right, let's get out and have a look.

Boss Yes, let's see what's up with . . . oh!

Billy Hey, there's a copper flat out on the roof! What shall we do?

Boss Run, boys. Just shut up and run!

The Safe

The Safe

Three characters: *Boss, Flash* and *Billy*

Boss   OK, boys, this is it.

Flash   This is the place, is it?

Boss   Yes, boys.

Billy   Are you sure, Boss? It's very dark in this street.

Flash   Yes, Boss, are you sure you've got the right place?

Boss   Yes, this is it. See, it tells us on that wall: SMITH'S WOODEN BOXES.

Flash   It's not that I don't trust you, but you're the only man I know who gets lost on a zebra crossing.

Boss   Look, I'm telling you, this is the place. The safe is in there, and it's stuffed full of money.

Flash   You're sure about the safe, Boss?

Billy   And the money?

Boss   Yes, for the last time, this is the place. The safe is in there and it's stuffed full of money. You see, it's pay-day tomorrow.

Flash	That's a bit daft, leaving the wages in the safe all night.
Billy	Yes, somebody might nick them.
Boss	What do you mean, 'Somebody might nick them'? *We're* going to nick them!
Billy	There you are, then. Old Smith should have more sense.
Flash	He's not the only one.
Boss	I wish you two would shut up. I don't know why he puts the money in the safe overnight. He just does. It's a fact. He's done it for years.
Flash	How do we get in, then?
Boss	In the door round the back. Then up the stairs to the office.
Billy	What about the alarms, Boss?
Boss	The alarms are old, and they're just fitted on the windows. They don't expect us to walk in the door.
Billy	How long have we got to do the job, Boss?
Boss	All night, Billy. It's only one o'clock now. It's a long time before the cleaners come in. And I happen to know one of the cleaners quite well.

Flash	So that's how you know about the safe, Boss?
Boss	You could say that, Flash.
Billy	Let's not hang about, Boss.
Boss	OK, here's the door. Let's get to work on the lock.
Flash	Let me have a go. I'll open it in no time.
Boss	OK, go on then.
Billy	It looks an old lock.
Flash	Yes it is, and it's a bit stiff.
Billy	Why don't you let me kick the door in?
Boss	Billy, we're crooks, not vandals.
Flash	I think we'll have to smash it.
Billy	I can do a bit of Kung Fu on it.
Boss	The lock won't open at all, then?
Flash	No, it's too stiff.
Billy	Go on, Boss, let me kick it.
Boss	Oh, go on then, if it will shut you up.
Flash	Come on then, Bruce Lee.
Billy	HEEEAAAGH!!!
	CRASH

Flash	That's very good, Billy. Your foot went right through.
Billy	But it won't come out.
Boss	What?
Billy	My foot's gone through the door, but it's stuck. It won't come out.
Boss	Well pull it.
Billy	I am pulling it.
Flash	You've put your foot in it this time, Billy.
Boss	Cut the jokes and help me pull him out.
Flash	Yes, Boss, sorry, Boss . . . three bags full, Boss.
Boss	Get hold of him. Now, pull.
Billy	Aagh!!
Flash	That's it.
Billy	You almost pulled my leg off!
Boss	You're lucky I didn't pull your head off. But at least that's got us a hole to poke a hand through. I can just reach the lock.
Flash	Let's get up to the office.
Billy	Where's the safe, Boss?
Flash	Here it is, over here.
Boss	Over here with the torch, Billy.

Billy	OK, Boss.
Boss	Yes, this is it.
Flash	It looks like a new safe, Boss.
Billy	Yes, Boss, I've never seen one like that before.
Boss	Relax, boys, your Boss is here. I just have to touch a safe and it opens. I've got brains in my fingers.
Flash	That must be why you've got none in your head.
Boss	What was that, Flash?
Flash	Nothing, Boss.
Billy	Give it a try then, Boss.
Boss	OK, Billy, stand back.
Billy	OK, Boss.
Boss	Now then, let's try a little turn this way, and then left, and then right. . . .
Billy	Have you got it, Boss?
Flash	Shut up, Billy, and just wait.
Boss	There we are, that'll do it, just turn the handle and. . . .
Flash	It's still locked.

Boss	Um, it's still locked.
Flash	Try again.
Boss	OK, here we go then. A turn to the left, then right, and left. . . .
Flash	Can't you get it open, Boss?
Boss	Well, if you put it that way, no. I can't get it open.
Billy	Why don't we blow it, Boss?
Boss	I'm no good at blowing safes, Billy.
Billy	I am, Boss. Remember when we did that big old house by the park?
Flash	Don't we all, Billy.
Billy	The time I blew the door off the safe!
Flash	You also blew the safe off the wall.
Boss	And the wall off the house. All the money in the safe was burned up.
Flash	It was just like bonfire night.
Billy	Well, it was my first try.
Boss	And your last, so shut up and think of something else.
Billy	How about my pen-knife?
Boss	What about your pen-knife?

Billy	It's very sharp and....
Flash	So you think you can cut a safe open with that thing, do you?
Billy	No. But it's got lots of other things on it too.
Boss	Like what?
Billy	Well, there's a screw-driver, and a thing to take stones out of a horse's hoof, and a....
Flash	We're not trying to steal a horse, Billy, we're trying to open a safe.
Billy	I'm only trying to help.
Boss	Well shut up. That'll be a big help.
Flash	What are we going to do then, Boss?
Boss	Let me think.
Flash	Don't rush now, Boss.
Billy	Take it easy, Boss.
Boss	I've got it!
Flash	It's OK, Boss. I had it one time, but I took tablets for it, and it went away.
Boss	Cut that out, will you? I've got it. If we can't get the money out of the safe, we'll just take the safe with the money in it.
Flash	You're going to take the safe away?

Boss	Yes. It's not too big, and it's not screwed down. I reckon the three of us can shift it. We'll take it over to my place. We'll have more time to open it there.
Billy	How will we get it over to your place, Boss? We haven't got a van any more.
Flash	Yes, we must be the only crooks on foot this side of the Great War.
Boss	I was just coming to that. We need another van. Billy, can you go out and pinch a van?
Billy	OK, Boss.
Flash	There's just one other thing, Boss. How are we going to get the safe down those stairs? They're very steep. It's a long way down with a safe.
Boss	Emm . . . yes. . . .
Flash	But just a minute, how do they get the boxes down from up here?
Boss	Through the loading-bay over there.
Flash	And how do they get them down from the loading-bay to the street?
Boss	With ropes, round those wheels.
Flash	So we could push the safe through to the loading-bay, and tie the safe to the ropes. Then let it down into the street.

Boss	Yes, I was just going to say that myself.
Flash	Charming.
Boss	Now you and me can start pushing the safe through the loading-bay. As soon as Billy gets back with the van, we'll get the safe down and away.
Flash	Wait a minute. What's that noise?
Boss	What noise?
Flash	Listen.
Boss	It's not just the noise of a van.
Flash	No. It's more like music.
Boss	It is music.
Flash	And it's coming this way.
Boss	It's like an ice-cream van.
Flash	It is an ice-cream van. Look, it's coming down the street.
Boss	What stupid idiot can be driving an ice-cream van round at two o'clock in the morning?
Flash	There's only one stupid idiot that I know.
Boss	Oh, no.
Flash	Oh, yes.
Boss	Billy!

Billy	Hello, Boss, is that you up there?
Boss	Shut up, Billy, of course it's us.
Flash	Who do you think it is, Batman and Robin?
Boss	And turn that music off. You'll have every copper for miles onto us!
Billy	Sorry, Boss.
Flash	What the heck did you pinch an ice-cream van for?
Billy	I felt like an ice-lolly.
Boss	You'll look like an ice-lolly by the time I've finished with you! Now get up here and give us a hand!
Billy	OK, Boss, here I come.
Flash	Now let's get that safe down into the street.
Boss	Have a look round for a bit of rope.
Billy	Here's some, Boss.
Boss	OK, now tie it round the safe.
Flash	I'll do it, Boss. I don't trust Billy. He can't even tie his shoe-laces.
Billy	Yes I can. It's getting my shoes on the right feet that's hard.
Boss	Now loop the rope round the wheel there, and let the end drop down into the street.

Flash	OK, now we need someone down in the street to hold the rope and let the safe down.
Billy	I'll do it, Boss.
Boss	No you won't. I don't trust you. I'll do it myself. Now when I pull hard on the rope you push the safe out of the door. Then I'll let the safe down into the street.
Billy	OK, Boss.
Flash	Come on, Billy, over here. Push hard when I tell you.
Billy	OK, Flash.
Flash	And watch what you're doing.
Billy	OK, Flash.
Flash	Are you down yet, Boss?
Boss	OK, Flash, push it out.
Flash	Right, Billy, push the safe out now . . . push . . . that's it. Down she goes.
Billy	What do we do now, Flash?
Flash	Go down and get it into the van.
Billy	I hope there's a lot of money inside it.
Flash	Come on, let's get down into the street.

Billy	Well here's the safe, but where's the Boss?
Flash	Boss, where are you?
Billy	Come on, Boss, don't say you've run off and left us.
Boss	I'm up here.
Flash	Where?
Boss	I'm up the blasted rope!
Billy	Hey look, Flash, he's up there hanging on the rope.
Flash	So he is.
Billy	What are you doing up there, Boss?
Boss	Waiting for a bus, you twit, what do you think I'm doing?
Flash	What *are* you doing up there, Boss?
Boss	Well I was down there holding the rope, right?
Billy	Right.
Boss	With the safe on the other end up here, right?
Flash	Right.
Boss	And you pushed the safe out, right?

Flash	Yes.
Boss	And the safe is heavy, right?
Billy	Yes.
Boss	And I'm not, right?
Flash	Right.
Boss	So the end of the rope with the safe on goes down. And the end with me on goes up.
Flash	Oh.
Boss	So that's why I'm up here on the end of this blasted rope. Hanging on for my life. So will you two clowns do something before I fall off and break my neck!
Flash	Go on, Billy, run up fast and help him.
Billy	OK, Flash.
Boss	Here he comes, it's rent-a-nut himself.
Billy	What do you want me to do, Boss?
Boss	Get out here and hang on to the end of this rope with me. Then we can both get down.
Billy	Right, Boss.
Boss	Come on, jump.
Billy	Here I come . . . got it.

Boss	You see, it's easy. Now you and me add up to more than the safe. So down we go.
Billy	Hey, we're going down. I feel like Tarzan.
Boss	With hair like that you look more like Jane.
Billy	Look out, down there. We're coming down.
Boss	That's it.
Flash	Well done, Boss. That was a nasty moment.
Billy	Can I let go of the rope now, Boss?
Boss	No, we must both hang on till we check the safe.
Billy	I'll hang on then, with you.
Boss	But where is the safe?
Flash	It's back up there.
Boss	What the heck's it doing up there?
Flash	Well, you've come down. So the safe on the other end has gone up.
Boss	Oh no, what are we going to do now?
Billy	It's easy, Boss. I just let go, like this.
Boss	No, Billy, don't. . . AAGHHH!!!
Billy	See, the safe's coming down.
Flash	And the boss is going up, you twit. What are we going to do now?

Billy	I've got an idea.
Flash	Go on then.
Boss	OK, action man, get on with it. What a nut he is!
Flash	He just wants to help, Boss.
Boss	I know what he wants. Treating me like a yo-yo.
Flash	He's back now, Boss.
Billy	I've done it. He'll be down in no time.
Flash	What have you done?
Billy	I rang the fire brigade.
Flash	What!
Billy	I rang the fire brigade. They'll get him down. They've got ladders.
Boss	The crazy fool! Get me down fast, and let's get out of here.
Billy	I'll get you down fast, Boss, with my pen-knife.
Flash	No, Billy, no!
Billy	It's very sharp. One hack at the rope and. . . .
Boss	No, Billy, don't!
Billy	. . . it's cut!

Boss	Billy . . . aaaAAAGGHHH!!?!*!
	CRASH
Boss	Ouch! Oh! Help! Oh! Oww!
Flash	Billy, give me a hand, pick him up, DO SOMETHING.
Billy	Don't worry, Boss, I'll save you. I'll go and get help.
Flash	Can you get up, Boss? How do you feel?
Boss	Not too bad. This leg's a bit sore, but I think I'm OK. I landed on my wallet.
Flash	We'd better get out of here. I'll get Billy.
Boss	Where is he, the little twit?
Flash	He's gone to get help.
Billy	It's OK, Boss, I rang for an ambulance, so you'll be OK
Flash	You rang for an ambulance!
Boss	What! First the fire brigade, then the ambulance. All we need now is the coppers and we can have a party.
Flash	Hey, Boss, I think that's them.
Billy	Yes, I can hear a cop car coming.
Boss	Oh no! Well, you hit the jackpot this

time, Billy. The fire brigade, the ambulance and the cops all in one go.

Flash   What shall we do, Boss?

Boss   Just leave everything, and get out of here fast.

Flash   Can you make it, Boss?

Boss   Yes, I'll be OK. It's just this leg that hurts a bit.

Billy   You'd better hop it then.

Flash   Very funny. Now let's do what the Boss says and run!

Billy   OK, but shouldn't we move the van first? It's parked on the double yellow lines. . . .